My birthday

My star sign

My biggest talent

My biggest secret

LIL BARBIE LIL BARBIE EDITION

All about my pet
If you don't have a pet,
write all about your
dream pet.

**Write about what you will be like in
the future, here!**

FUTURE IS BRIGHT

Barbie

A walk in the park

START

Help Barbie and her puppy pal to get through the park.

FINISH

Contents

...shed 2022.

...Brother Books Ltd, Ground Floor, 23 Southernhay East, Exeter, Devon EX1 1QL

...d in the United Kingdom.

...@littlebrotherbooks.co.uk

...ittlebrotherbooks.co.uk

...ttle Brother Books trademark, email and website addresses, are the sole and exclusive ...ties of Little Brother Books Limited.

...s used under license from Shutterstock.

Barbie

ALL ABOUT ME

Fill in this journal with info all about you!

Doodle your name here ⟶ ....

My three favourite things to do are

1.

2.

3.

My three favourite things about school are

1.

2.

3.

Pet perfection

Tick off all the things you need to do to look after your pet perfectly.

Feed them regularly

Give them plenty of food

Keep them clean

Leave them on their own a lot

Take them to the vet when they are poorly

Play with them

Feed them leftovers

Is there anything we've forgotten? Write in your own ideas, too!

_____

_____

BARBIE
brainbox
Did you know that cats were the world's most popular pet in 2021?

5

Soccer SKILLS

Barbie's team are well on their way to winning their first ever championship! They need a new kit for the final.

Can you design it for them?

Secret Formula!

Can you work out the missing part of the formula using the code below?

Adding two parts hydrogen to one part **? 9 1 @ * 2**

_____ _____ _____ _____ _____ _____

will create **$ % + * 5**

_____ _____ _____ _____ _____

% - A   * - E

@ - G   2 - N

? - O   5 - R

+ - T $ - W

9 - X   1 - Y

Music mix up

Unscramble the letters to work out these different types of music.

CSALASICL
....

OPP
....

RCOK
....

ZAJZ
....

PIH POH
....

BAKE OFF

Fit each of these baking bits into the grid. Each item can only appear once in each row, column and mini square.

FUTURE YOU!

Ever wondered what the future may hold?

Grab your dice to discover what might be in store.

The best bit? If you don't like your 'future' you can always roll the dice and start again!

MY JOB WILL BE:

1 – Doctor
2 – Scientist
3 – Author
4 – Musician
5 – Teacher
6 – Chef

I WILL LIVE IN:

1 – A tree house
2 – A cottage in the woods
3 – A fancy apartment
4 – A mansion
5 – A boat
6 – A house

AT THE WEEKENDS I LIKE TO:

1 – Paint
2 – Run marathons
3 – Help at an animal shelter
4 – Watch movies
5 – Read books
6 – Play soccer

I WILL GET AROUND ON/IN:

1 – A scooter
2 – A car
3 – A motorcycle
4 – A bicycle
5 – A horse and carriage
6 – My own two legs!

WRITE YOUR OWN DESTINY!
Use this space to write your own dream future. It can be anything you want! Brooklyn has done hers already.

My job:
Music producer

My house:
A New York penthouse

My dream mode of transport:
Chauffeur-driven limo
(or I'll hop on the subway)

My hobby:
Chilling out with my friends
– or singing!

My job:

My house:

My dream mode of transport:

My hobby:

ORDER UP!

Brooklyn and Malibu are helping out at Buddy's café and some friends have come to see them!

Complete the puzzles to work out who has ordered what.

Rafa has been doodling costume designs on his order ticket. Can you find the hidden words in his drawings?

PINEAPPLE SMOOTHIE

GRILLED CHEESE

Uh-oh, Jayla and Jackson have spilled water over their order. Can you work out what they want?

I_E C___M
S_NDAE

Brooklyn and Malibu's mums have popped in to see their girls hard at work. They've decided to give them an extra challenge by mixing up the letters in their order. Unscramble them to find out what they want.

BERGUR & FIERS

SAHTPGETI

STRONG VIBES only!

Decorate the page below with a message you feel strongly about.

When people feel strongly that something should change, they go on marches and paint placards to show their message to the world.

STRONG GIRLS MAKE WAVES

UNITE · be kind · STRONG · Barbie

BETTER TOGETHER

BARBIE

art with flavour

Finish off the picture Barbie's friend is painting by joining the dots. Can you work out what it is? Use your brightest paints or pens to bring it to life!

DESIGN A DOOR

If you want everyone to know exactly which room is yours, create a cool door sign with 3D lettering.

First, learn how to create this awesome effect!

1. Draw your letters in capitals in a square, boxy style.

2. Draw short lines from each point of your letter. Make sure they are all going in the same direction.

3. Join the short lines up using straight lines.

4. Shade in your letter. Make sure the 3D parts of your letter are a slightly darker shade to the front part of your letter - this will help it to stand out!

Design a front and a back then carefully cut it out, fold down the middle and glue together.

SIGN

Make sure you have read page 18 before you cut out your door hanger. If you don't want to cut up your book, photocopy or scan and print this page instead.

Hello hobbies!

Tick all the things you have done in one pen, then tick everything you would love to try in a different pen.

DREAM ROBOT

If you could design your own robot, what would it do?

What would it look like?

What would you call it?

Use the space below to create your own design!

LIMITED EDITION BARBIE

Robot name:

Special abilities:

WHICH GUITAR?

Barbie is about to perform on stage, but the wires on her guitar are tangled together!

Can you work out which one is hers?

A

B

C

BARBIE *brainbox*
Guitars were played in Ancient Egypt!

Sleepover checklist

Use this page to tick off all the things you would love at your next sleepover.

WHAT'S YOUR ADVENTURE?

Start here

Love to travel? → Sometimes

↓ Yes

Interested in science? → It's not my favourite

↓ Totally!

Feeling brave? → Sometimes

↓ Always!

SPACE ADVENTURE

The sky is not the limit for your adventuring – you want to smash through the sky and head to the stars! You are brave, ambitious and curious.

Answer the questions and follow the flowchart to see what your Barbie adventure could be!

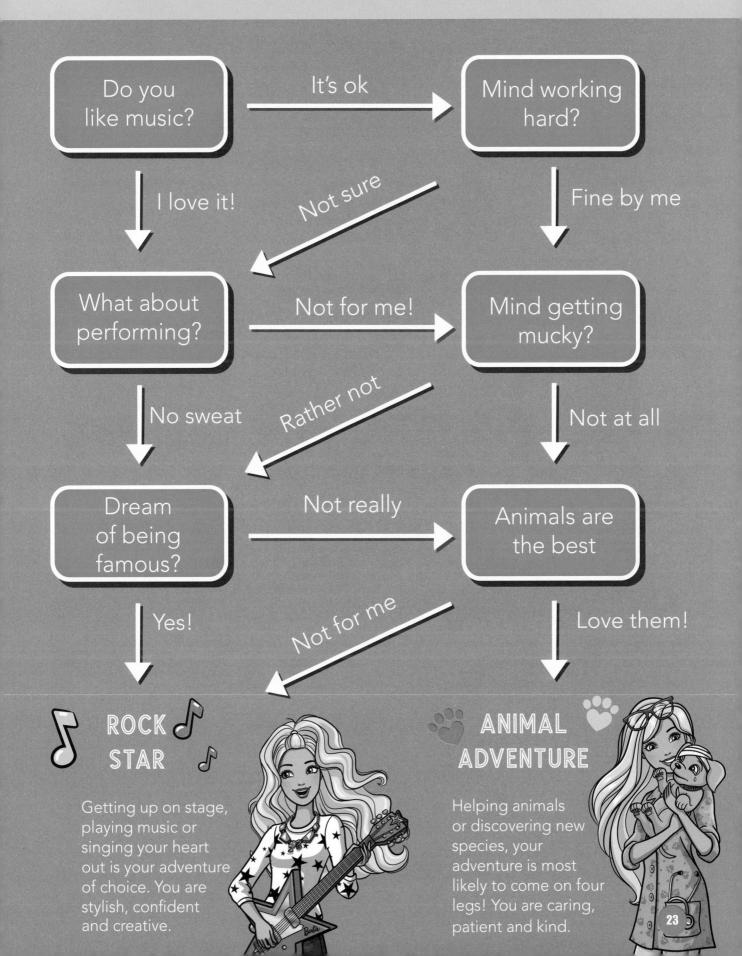

Do you like music?

It's ok →

Mind working hard?

I love it! ↓

Not sure ↙

Fine by me ↓

What about performing?

Not for me! →

Mind getting mucky?

No sweat ↓

Rather not ↙

Not at all ↓

Dream of being famous?

Not really →

Animals are the best

Yes! ↓

Not for me ↙

Love them! ↓

ROCK STAR

Getting up on stage, playing music or singing your heart out is your adventure of choice. You are stylish, confident and creative.

ANIMAL ADVENTURE

Helping animals or discovering new species, your adventure is most likely to come on four legs! You are caring, patient and kind.

23

What's missing?

Take a look at the pictures of Barbie's dreamhouse, below. Some items have gone missing in the second picture! Can you work out what they are?

There are 8 to find.

Tick a box every time you find a difference!

1 2 3 4 5 6 7 8

Find your inner calm

When you've had a busy day,
or you just feel a little out of sorts,
use these calming techniques to
help you feel zen again.

Talk about your day

Stretch your arms up high and out wide.

Go for a walk

Read

Have a warm bath

Take three deep breaths in through your mouth and out through your nose.

Ballet practice

FIND ALL OF THESE BALLET WORDS IN THE GRID.
WATCH OUT!
THEY CAN GO FORWARDS, BACKWARDS, UP, DOWN AND DIAGONALLY!

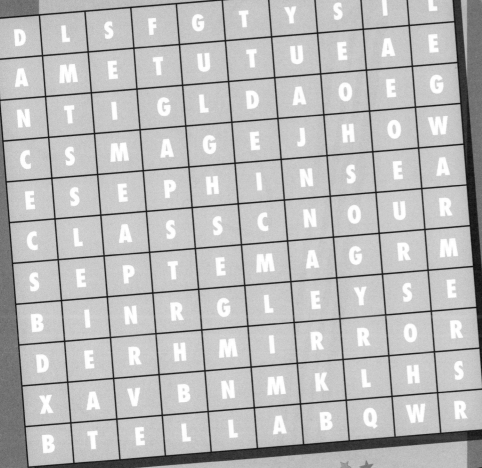

D	L	S	F	G	T	Y	S	I	L
A	M	E	T	U	T	U	E	A	E
N	T	I	G	L	D	A	O	E	G
C	S	M	A	G	E	J	H	O	W
E	S	E	P	H	I	N	S	E	A
C	L	A	S	S	C	N	O	U	R
S	E	P	T	E	M	A	G	R	M
B	I	N	R	G	L	E	Y	S	E
D	E	R	H	M	I	R	R	O	R
X	A	V	B	N	M	K	L	H	S
B	T	E	L	L	A	B	Q	W	R

- [ ] BALLET
- [ ] BARRE
- [ ] CLASS
- [ ] DANCE
- [ ] LEGGINGS
- [ ] LEGWARMERS
- [ ] MIRROR
- [ ] SHOES
- [ ] TUTU

PLAN A BESTSELLER!

EVER WISHED YOU COULD BE AN AUTHOR?

Now you can plan your very own novel!

Design your front cover and write down what your story will be like.

Book title:

My characters will be called:

Where it will be set:

What will happen:

Fashion mix up

Barbie and her friends have had a clothes catastrophe!
Match up their tops, bottoms and shoes
so that they all fit together.

BROOKLYN AND MALIBU'S FRIENDSHIP FILES

When Brooklyn met Malibu they became firm friends for life. They support each other's dreams and make each other laugh.

Use this page to write about the special people in your life!

The person who gives great advice is:

The person who supports me the most is:

I have learnt a lot from:

I love playing with:

The person who always makes me feel safe is:

I think I am a great friend to:

The person who makes me laugh the most is:

MEET *BARBIE'S*

Ever imagined you could step into Barbie's world?

Read along the charts to see what character you might be!

Barbie

B

Your first name would be

YOUR EYE COLOUR	
BLUE	ACE
BROWN	HARPER
GREEN	ALEX
HAZEL	CRUZ
GREY	JJ

Your second name would be

YOUR HAIR COLOUR	
BLONDE	ROBINSON
BROWN	FERNANDEZ
BLACK	LEE
RED	SINGH

Barbie

My name would be

_____

NEW BFF!

Your biggest talent would be

YOUR BIRTH MONTH

JANUARY	SINGING
FEBRUARY	CODING
MARCH	WRITING
APRIL	SKATEBOARDING
MAY	SURFING
JUNE	VLOGGING
JULY	PAINTING
AUGUST	SWIMMING
SEPTEMBER	DANCING
OCTOBER	HORSE RIDING
NOVEMBER	MATHS
DECEMBER	ACTING

Your friends say they love you because you are

YOUR BIRTH DATE

1-5	FUNNY
6-10	KIND
11-15	CARING
16-20	LOYAL
21-25	SUPPORTIVE
26-31	HELPFUL

You first met Barbie

THE COLOUR TOP YOU ARE WEARING

BLUE	AT SCHOOL
RED	IN NEW YORK
YELLOW	AT THE BEACH
GREEN	IN A DINER
ORANGE	OUT SHOPPING
PURPLE	THROUGH HER VLOG
WHITE	WALKING YOUR DOGS
BLACK	ON HOLIDAY
MULTI COLOURED	VOLUNTEERING
PINK	PLAYING SOCCER

INTO THE WILD

Barbie loves photographing the cute animals she meets. What has she found this time?

Use the space to draw in your favourite creature.

My family tree

Barbie and her sisters love being a family and Jayla and Jackson think it is cool they have two dads. Each family is special, no matter how many members it has or how it is put together.

Use the circles above to draw a picture of all the people who make up your family.

PLANET REPORT

Barbie has taken a trip to the stars and discovered a new planet!

Fill in her report To describe your own dream planet.

REPORT

I have discovered a new planet!
It is called _____.
The trees aren't brown or green
like on earth, they are _____ and
_____and the sky is
_____. The creatures who live here look
like_____and
they eat_____. The air smells like
_____ and
instead of water, they have rivers flowing
with_____.

Marvellous mermaids

Spot the **seven** differences between these pictures of the mermaid BFFs.

Special day

Make this birthday picture magical and design an outfit for Barbie to wear on her special day.

PICTURE THIS!

Match the close ups to these pictures of Barbie and her friends. Draw a line between each close up and the picture it belongs to.

WE ARE FAMILY

Epiphany was standing patiently waiting for Rafa to decide how he would like his muffin to be cooked, when suddenly, Brooklyn and Malibu burst through the diner doors.

"We did it!" said Brooklyn. "We just got paid for our last gig, so as of right now we have enough money to pay for our first full studio session!"

Brooklyn and Malibu were desperate to record their new song at Blown Speaker Studios. As soon as they had, they were going to send it to a top record producer.

"This is huge!" said Rafa, opening up his laptop. "OK, manager time!"

Brooklyn and Malibu settled into the booth with Rafa, just as Epiphany magically laid two breakfasts in front of them. As they tucked in, Rafa spoke into his phone. "Lyla! Need to get my two superstars into the studio, pronto!"

Brooklyn and Malibu watched as Rafa's face went from excited to disappointed. Blown Speaker Studios was suffering a major power outage and it wouldn't be ready for them until 3pm.

The two friends decided to practice at Brooklyn's house until it was time to go to the studio. They were just about to go over their vocal warm-ups, when Jackson and Jayla, Brooklyn's twin neighbours, came in.

"Hello Senseis for the day!" said Jackson.

Malibu looked puzzled.

"Don't worry, he always talks like that after Karate,"said Jayla.

Brooklyn's mum Simone followed the twins into Brooklyn's room. She was wearing her pilots' uniform and carrying a briefcase. "I have to take over a last-minute flight," she said. "So I need you to…"

"Watch the twins?!" Brooklyn said, horrified.

"Knew you'd understand!" said Simone, kissing her daughter goodbye and dashing off to the airport.

Jackson grinned. "That's what I meant by Senseis for the day!" he said.

Brooklyn and Malibu stared at each other. They had a recording session booked in for 3pm and now they would have to bring Jackson and Jayla with them.

On the way to the studio, Brooklyn read out a list of rules for Jackson and Jayla. "No playing. No flipping. No fighting…" she began in her best mum-voice.

The twins grinned back at them. Today was going to be so much more fun than they had imagined.

At the studio, Lyla showed Brooklyn and Malibu into the room they would be recording in. At a huge desk filled with dials and buttons, sat Chuck, their engineer. It was his job to record Brooklyn and Malibu's song. He waved hello as he took a big bite out of a doughnut, dripping jam all down his shirt.

Brooklyn settled Jackson and Jayla on the little sofa in the corner of the room while Malibu set up the microphones. They waved to Chuck, who hit the record button and he began to count them in. "Five, four, three, two…" Chuck began. "STOP! What's that crunching sound?"

Everyone's eyes were drawn to the couch where Jackson was munching on a bag of crisps.

"Where did you even find them?" Brooklyn said.

"In the bass drum over there!" Jackson said. "Besides the fuzz, they're tasty!"

"Ewww!" said Malibu as Brooklyn snatched the mouldy bag of crisps from Jackson's hand.

"I hope you packed plenty of snacks," said Jayla. "Or else he'll just keep finding things on the floor to eat."

Malibu and Brooklyn put their heads together for a team huddle. They were going to have to order some food in from Epiphany's diner to keep the twins happy. "Problem solved!" said Malibu as she punched the number into her phone.

At that moment, the door to the studio swung open and, to Malibu's amazement, Chelsea, Skipper and Stacie appeared.

"Surprise!" they all shouted together.

After the sisters had let Malibu go from their big welcome hug, they explained just what they were doing in New York: "Mum and Dad have been planning this surprise sister-visit for weeks!" said Skipper. "When you said you were recording today, we came straight here from the airport!"

Malibu was thrilled to see her sisters, she missed them now that she was living away from home, but she also knew that there was only a short time left in the recording studio.

With Jackson, Jayla, Skipper, Stacie and Chelsea squeezed together on the studio couch, Brooklyn and Malibu were ready to start recording.

Chuck pressed record once again and… everything went dark. The studio's circuit board blew. Again. "Lyla!" Chuck shouted.

As Lyla managed to get everything working again, Epiphany finally turned up at the studios with armfuls of sandwiches, drinks and bags of crisps. When Lyla showed her in to Malibu and Brooklyn's booth, a cheer erupted.

"I want turkey!" said Jackson.

"I want ham!" cried Jayla.

"I want crisps!" called Stacie.

Brooklyn glanced at Malibu with a big grin. "Hurry! Let's get to work while their mouths are busy chewing!"

Finally, Brooklyn and Malibu began to perform their song. Chuck nodded along to the music as he adjusted the dials and buttons on his control desk.

Skipper looked over at the desk from her sandwich. She couldn't help but be impressed by the technology on display. "Hmm," she said, looking over Chuck's shoulder. "I think it needs more bass." With that, Skipper turned the bass dial up as far as it would go. With a loud bang, the control desk sparked and everything went dark once again. "Lyla!" shouted Chuck.

Brooklyn and Malibu had run out of patience. Now the food was finished, all the kids had begun squabbling.

"Time for another team huddle?" asked Brooklyn. Malibu nodded. "But this time, it should be with *all* of us."

Brooklyn and Malibu knew that the only way they were going to get their song recorded was by *including* their family, instead of getting them to be quiet. They put Jackson and Jayla on backing vocals, Stacie on maracas, Chelsea on percussion and Skipper was given one button to press on the control board. "Just this one," warned Chuck. "NONE of the others."

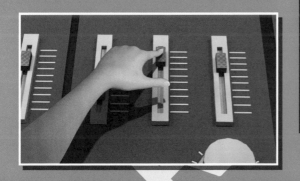

With that, Chuck counted down one more time and Brooklyn and Malibu began to sing. This time everything went to plan.

When the song was finally finished, a peaceful calm settled over the studio. Everyone looked at Chuck. "LYLA!!!" he screamed once more. Lyla came rushing into the studio to see what had gone wrong now. "We have a hit!" Chuck said.

THE END

Quiz time!

Can you solve all these questions?
You'll find all the answers somewhere in this book!

1. What are the names of Malibu's sisters?

2. What does Brooklyn's mum do for a job?

3. What are four things you should do to look after a pet properly?

4. What is the name of Malibu and Brooklyn's friend who loves designing fashion?

5. Name three types of music!

6. What is the name of the café Epiphany works in?

Answers

Page 4 A walk in the park

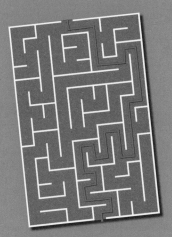

Page 5 Pet Perfection

Feed them regularly.

Keep them clean.

Take them to the vet when they are poorly.

Play with them.

Page 7 Secret formula!

?91@*2
OXYGEN

$%+*5
WATER

Page 8 Music mix up

OPP = POP

CSALASICL = CLASSICAL

PIH POH = HIP HOP

ZAJZ = JAZZ

RCOK = ROCK

Page 9 Bake off

Page 12 Order up!

PINEAPPLE SMOOTHIE
GRILLED CHEESE

Page 13

ICE CREAM SUNDAE
BURGER & FRIES
SPAGHETTI

Page 15 Art with flavour

Page 20 Which guitar?

Guitar B

Page 24 What's missing?

Answers

Page 27 Ballet practice

Page 29 Fashion mix up

Page 37
Marvellous mermaids

Page 39 Picture this!

Page 46 Quiz Time!

1. Chelsea, Skipper and Stacie.

2. Brooklyn's mum is a pilot.

3. Feed them regularly.
   Keep them clean.
   Take them to the vet when they are poorly.
   Play with them.

4. Rafa.

5. Possible answers could be: jazz, hip hip, pop, rock and classical.

6. Buddy's Cafe.